Welcome Home!

by
DIK BROWNE

First published 1988 by Attica Publications.

Attica Limited,
DLM House,
Edinburgh Way,
Harlow, Essex, CM20 2HL
England.

ISBN 1 85176 173 X

Printed in Hong Kong

HÄGAR
HELGA
HONI
I AIN'T EVEN RELATED
LUCKY EDDIE
KVACK
HAMLET
SNERT
HERNIA

OKAY, HAGAR, TAKE A DEEP BREATH AND ADMIT NOTHING !!

OH, HI, HONEY... AM I LATE ?

BEFORE YOU SAY A WORD, LET ME WARN YOU—*DON'T TRY TO LIE TO ME!*

BECAUSE IF A VIKING TELLS A LIE HIS HORNS WILL FALL OFF!!
NOW, WHERE WERE YOU?!
OUT

YOU STOPPED TO HAVE A DRINK, DIDN'T YOU?
NO... I DIDN'T STOP TO HAVE **A** DRINK...

DON'T BE SMART! YOU'VE BEEN BOOZING IT UP WITH YOUR NO-GOOD FRIENDS! HAVEN'T YOU? HAVEN'T YOU?

ANSWER YES OR NO!
4-4
DIK BROWNE

NO!
© King Features Syndicate, Inc., 1976. World rights reserved.

WHAT A DUMP!
GENTLY, HAGAR, GENTLY. THIS IS A CLASSIC LAND

WHY IS IT SO BEAT UP?
THAT'S CALLED ANTIQUITY

HEY! WHAT'S THAT?
SHH... IT'S A SCHOOL OF PHILOSOPHERS
© King Features Syndicate, Inc., 1976. World rights reserved.

WHAT'S PHILOSOPHY ?
THE STUDY OF ALL TRUTH AND KNOWLEDGE IN MAN'S EXPERIENCE SO THAT A DEEPER UNDERSTANDING OF OUR UNIVERSE IS POSSIBLE...
DIK BROWNE

WOW! ARE THEY DOING IT NOW ?
YES...LET'S NOT DISTURB THEM—

YOUR TURN TO COOK TONIGHT
NO, 'TISN'T
YES, 'TIS!
AW! GRIPE, GRIPE, GRIPE!
6-27

I'M TIRED! WE'VE BEEN HIKING FOR DAYS!!
COMPLAINTS! COMPLAINTS! OKAY, WE'LL SLEEP A WHILE!

WE'RE NOT GOING TO SLEEP ON THIS HARD, COLD GROUND, ARE WE?
YAWN
WHY NOT?! VIKINGS ARE TOUGH!!

?

KLUNK!

I CAN'T SLEEP WITHOUT A PILLOW

SOFTIE!

GOSH, HAGAR, ISN'T IT TERRIBLY DARK?
WHAT DO YOU EXPECT—THESE ARE THE **DARK AGES**

THE NIGHT IS FULL OF STRANGE SOUNDS
OOOOOOOH
HOOOO
AWK

ANIMALS FLEE WHEN NONE PURSUE THEM

THE BIRDS ARE SILENT AND THERE IS BLOOD ON THE MOON

THE SIGNS SAY THAT SOMETHING TERRIBLE IS ABOUT TO HAPPEN!
AW, I DON'T BELIEVE THAT BUNK!

YOU'RE JUST IN TIME FOR YOUR ANNUAL BATH

NOW QUIET, SNERT, WE DON'T WANT TO WAKE ANYBODY...

HELGA?

OKAY, SNEAKY! WHERE HAVE YOU BEEN?!!

AND REMEMBER — IF YOU TELL A LIE, YOUR HORNS WILL FALL OFF!

OKAY, I'LL TELL YOU....I'M LATE BECAUSE I HELPED AN OLD LADY ACROSS A STREET....

...AND SHE GAVE ME A MAGIC RING WHICH LED ME TO A TREASURE, BUT BANDITS STOLE IT AND I CHASED THEM TO ETHIOPIA WHERE A *DRAGON*...

POP!
POP!
POP!
POP!
PLUNK!
PLUNK!
SNAP!
POP
POP

I'VE LOOKED EVERYWHERE BUT I CAN'T FIND IT ANYWHERE.

I HATE TO DO THIS! HAGAR IS GOING TO BE FURIOUS!

HAGAR!

HAGAR!
PARDON ME — THAT'S THE WIFE.

WHAT?

WHERE IS THE KEY?
IN THE DESK!

I FOUND IT, THANKS!
DIDN'T I ASK YOU NOT TO CALL ME AT WORK?

IT WAS AN EMERGENCY!
SORRY ABOUT THAT.
FORGET IT— I'M MARRIED, TOO.

NOW... WHERE WERE WE?
OH, YEAH...

BAM!
SLASH!

BLAT!
HAGAR! HURRY UP AND GET DRESSED! YOU'LL MISS YOUR BOAT!!

I CAN'T FIND MY LACES.
YOU'RE STANDING ON THEM, STUPID!!

I CAN'T FIND DAD'S SHIELD.
LOOK IN THE BARN!
I FOUND DADDY'S SWORD!

HERE'S YOUR SHIELD, DAD.
THANKS...WHERE'S MY HAT?
ON YOUR HEAD, DUMMY.

NO, NO — THIS WAY! THAT'S A CLOSET!
OH.

WHERE IS DADDY GOING ?
TO FIND THE NEW WORLD.
HØLY ØDIN! DID HE LOSE THAT, TOO ?!!

COULD IT BE A SONG I HEAR ?
A JOLLY SONG...
AND GETTING NEAR

TA RA TA RE TRALA!

BEHOLD! THE TREASURES OF MY LIFE — MY BOY, MY GIRL, MY LOVING WIFE.

HONI OF THE GOLDEN HAIR, GEM-BRIGHT HAMLET— WHAT A PAIR !

AND THE CROWNING JEWEL OF ALL... HELGA, LOVELY, SWEET AND TALL...

OH WHAT JOY OH WHAT GLEE HO HA LUCKY LUCKY ME
DOES THAT HAPPEN VERY OFTEN ?
NOT OFTEN...

... ONLY WHEN THE MOON AND HAGAR ARE FULL AT THE SAME TIME...

I'M READY TO GO NOW, HELGA
DID YOU PUT ON CLEAN SOCKS?
YES

AND DO YOU HAVE YOUR LUNCH?
YES
ALL RIGHT. HAVE A NICE DAY.

WELL, I'M OFF TO CONQUER EUROPE
OH, BEFORE YOU GO—CAN YOU STOP AT THE OLSENS' AND BORROW A CUP OF SUGAR FOR ME?

ARE YOU NUTS? I GOT A THOUSAND MEN WAITING FOR ME!
IT WILL ONLY TAKE A MINUTE... DON'T ARGUE!

BUT THE INVASION...
IT'S RIGHT ON YOUR WAY...STOP WASTING TIME!!

WHAT DOES HE WANT?
A CUP OF SUGAR
WELL, HE DOESN'T HAVE TO BE SO TOUGH ABOUT IT!
8-1
© King Features Syndicate, Inc., 1978. World rights reserved.
DIK BROWNE

THIS WIND AND RAIN CAN'T LAST! IT HAS TO CHANGE!
I KNOW...

NOW IT'S SNOWING...

WE'LL HIDE IN THIS CAVE UNTIL THE STORM'S OVER!

BOY! THIS IS DARK! I CAN'T SEE A THING!

IT'S CREEPY!

AND WET!
AND COLD!

QUIT COMPLAINING! AT LEAST IT'S GOT WALL-TO-WALL CARPETING!

MY APPETITE HAS BEEN
A LITTLE OFF LATELY...

AND I WAS
THINKING...
NO!

NO, YOU CAN'T HAVE A DRINK
BEFORE DINNER!

YOU BE THINKING ABOUT WHAT
YOU WANT FOR DINNER

HMMM... LET ME THINK... WHAT WOULD I LIKE FOR DINNER?...

THAT'S A GOOD QUESTION... A REALLY GOOD QUESTION!

KVAKK

WELL? WHAT DO YOU WANT FOR DINNER?
DUCK SOUP!!

WHAT ARE YOU DOING WITH THAT BONE?
I'M TRAINING MY DOG SNERT

OKAY, BUT PUT IT BACK IN THE SOUP WHEN YOU'RE FINISHED

NOW, WHEN I SAY 'HEEL'— REMEMBER TO HEEL!
HEEL!

NO! NO! NOT 'HEAD'! HEEL!
THE POOR THING DOESN'T UNDERSTAND

THE ONLY WAY YOU CAN TRAIN HIM IS BY EXAMPLE — YOU SHOW SNERT HOW TO DO IT

SEE SNERT? SEE HAGAR? NOW WATCH WHAT HAGAR DOES!

HEEL!
VOOF!

THAT DOES IT! I'M NEVER GOING TO GET MARRIED!

HÄGAR!

ARE YOU AWAKE?
I AM NOW...

DID YOU HAVE A GOOD NIGHT?
EAT YOUR BREAKFAST WHILE IT'S HOT
WHAT TIME WILL YOU BE HOME?

STOP!

EVERY DAY YOU SAY THE SAME THINGS! YOU DON'T EVEN THINK OF WHAT YOU'RE SAYING ANYMORE!

I'M SORRY– I DIDN'T REALIZE I WAS DOING THAT...
I'M GOING TO WORK

HAVE A NICE DAY

IS IT BAD TO BRAG, DAD?
NAW

IT'S ESSENTIAL!

KID, IF YOU'RE GOING TO BE A VIKING, YOU'LL HAVE TO LEARN HOW TO BRAG

YOU LOOK THE ENEMY IN THE EYE AND DO THE 'CHICKEN SCRATCH' AND THEN YOU...

"OOWAWEEEE!!"
MY MOMMA WAS A THUNDERHEAD! MY DADDY WAS A LIGHTNING BOLT!

I'M MEANER THAN A SORE-TOOTH SNAKE... ROUGHER THAN A RUSTY SAW!

I SPIT NAILS AND I CAN BEAT ANY MAN IN THE WORLD!!

THEN YOU FIGHT?
HECK, KID—IF YOU DO IT RIGHT YOU DON'T HAVE TO FIGHT AT ALL!

DANCES TODAY ARE CRAZY

YOU'D NEVER CATCH ME DANCING LIKE THAT
I KNOW...

YEAH!
'RAY!
'RAY!

MY FOOT WAS ASLEEP
DIK BROWNE 4-25

A LOT OF PEOPLE THINK THE WORLD IS ROUND.
CRACKPOTS!

THE WORLD IS FLAT! THAT'S A FACT, NO MATTER WHAT THE LUNATIC FRINGE SAYS!

YOU WANT TO PROVE THE WORLD IS FLAT? ALL YOU GOTTA DO IS USE GOOD OLD VIKING LOGIC.

OBSERVE—
I AM FLAT!

THIS BEER IS FLAT.

MY FEET ARE FLAT!

ERGO! IT FOLLOWS: THE WHOLE WORLD IS FLAT!!

NOW, OF COURSE—
ON THE OTHER HAND...
12-14
DIK BROWNE
© King Features Syndicate, Inc., 1975. World rights reserved.

MAMA SAYS THE TIME HAS COME FOR ME TO HAVE A TALK WITH YOU.
ABOUT WHAT?

HOW I SHOULD GO ABOUT PICKING A MATE...
OH! I CAN TELL YOU THAT!

MY SON, IN CHOOSING A MATE THERE ARE *THREE* THINGS YOU SHOULD LOOK FOR...

FIRST– *STRENGTH*– THAT'S THE MOST IMPORTANT THING! *BIG, FAT MUSCLES!!*

AND HAIR — LOTTSA HAIR — ALL OVER THE LEGS AND ARMS!

AND SHARP TEETH... NOT MANY, BUT SHARP LIKE DAGGERS!!

HEY! WHERE ARE YOU GOING?!!

I DIDN'T TELL YOU HOW TO PICK THE REST OF THE CREW!
5-9
DIK BROWNE

THEY. SAID IT WOULDN'T RAIN TODAY...
THEY ALWAYS DO.

WELL, IT HAS TO END SOMETIME.
I'M BORED—THERE'S NOTHING TO DO!
HOW ABOUT A SWIM?

WHEN ARE WE GOING TO HAVE OUR SUMMER PICNIC?
WHEN IT STOPS RAINING.
WHAT A NEIGHBORHOOD! RAIN, RAIN, RAIN!!

WELL, YOU WOULDN'T HAVE TO WORRY ABOUT RAIN IF YOU HAD CONQUERED ITALY LIKE I ASKED YOU TO— BUT WOULD YOU? OH, NO!
AW!

HEY! IT STOPPED RAINING!

OUT! OUT! EVERYBODY OUT! ENJOY THE SUMMER!

TOO LATE!
12-7
DIK BROWNE
© King Features Syndicate, Inc., 1975. World rights reserved.

SHALL WE STOP FOR A BIT OF REFRESHMENT ?

A TABLE FOR TWO AND SOMETHING MILD TO DRINK.

SO THIS IS THE KIND OF PLACE YOU HANG OUT IN !!
ARE YOU KIDDING ? I'M AS SHOCKED AS YOU ARE !

DO YOU THINK I'D TAKE YOU HERE IF I KNEW THAT IT WAS LIKE **THIS** ?!

THEY SHOULD HAVE A SIGN OUT FRONT TO WARN INNOCENT PEOPLE!

NOW LET US GET OUT OF THIS DUMP!

PUT IT ON MY TAB.
8-3
DIK BROWNE
© King Features Syndicate, Inc., 1975. World rights reserved.

THE TROUBLE WITH US IS WE GOT NO CLASS

TAKE THE ENGLISH! — EVERYBODY IS A LORD OR A SIR OR A KNIGHT....

WHY CAN'T WE BE KNIGHTS?
WE CAN'T BECAUSE WE'RE NOT ENGLISH.
WE CAN DO ANYTHING THEY CAN DO!

YOU JUST TELL ME WHAT TO DO!
ME FIRST!
NO! ME!

THE KNIGHT-TO-BE APPROACHES HIS LORD WHO DUBS HIM ON HIS SHOULDER WITH THE FOLLOWING WORDS...
© King Features Syndicate, Inc., 1975. World rights reserved.

I DUB THEE...
I DUB THEE...
SWOOSH!

SIR GUSSIE
SIR GUSSIE...
AWOOOH!

NO......YOU JUST DON'T HAVE THAT NICE LIGHT TOUCH THE ENGLISH HAVE.
DIK BROWNE
4-13

BOY! WHAT A NERVE!

OH, YEAH ?!

NEITHER ARE YOU!

AND NEITHER ARE YOU!

DIK BROWNE
?
OR YOU!
?

AND NEITHER ARE YOU!

© King Features Syndicate, Inc., 1975. World rights reserved.
OR YOU!
WHAT'S DADDY SO MAD ABOUT?
OH... I JUST TOLD HIM HE WASN'T AS YOUNG AS HE USED TO BE.
7-27

I WILL NOT!
THAT'S WHAT YOU THINK!

IT'S THE LEAST YOU CAN DO! I'M DOING ALL THE REST!

LET ME OUT OF THIS DRESS!
SHUT UP! YOU WANT ME TO LOOK NICE, DON'T YOU?!

WHEN THE MATCHMAKER COMES TO LOOK OVER OUR DAUGHTER, HE SHOULDN'T FIND HER MAMA IN RAGS!!

HOLD THOSE FLOWERS — I'LL BE RIGHT BACK!
© King Features Syndicate, Inc., 1975. World rights reserved.

SOMEONE'S AT THE DOOR!
AW, NEVER MIND — I'LL GET IT!
KNOCK
KNOCK
4-27

WELL?
AAWKKK!!
DIK BROWNE..

MATCHMAKER! MATCHMAKER! COME BACK! IT'S A MISTAKE! THAT WASN'T OUR DAUGHTER!
ROW! KEEP ROWING!

HE'S HERE! ACT NICE! I'LL GET THE DOOR!

WHY, MR. GOOM! WHAT A SURPRISE!

MR. GOOM—THIS IS OUR BEAUTIFUL, TALENTED AND AS YET UNMARRIED DAUGHTER, HONI.

VERY NICE TO MEET YOU...

COULD THE YOUNG LADY RUN AROUND THE ROOM A FEW TIMES?

GOOD WIND! THAT'S IMPORTANT.
6-1 DIK BROWNE

GOOD TEETH! YOU CAN TELL A LOT FROM TEETH. NOW LIFT YOUR FOOT.

HEY! WHAT BUSINESS WERE YOU IN BEFORE YOU BECAME A MARRIAGE BROKER?

LUM DE DUM DUM

DUM DE DUM DUM
OH, YOU KID!

BOY, ARE YOU GETTING FAT!

I AM NOT FAT! I'M BIG! DO YOU HEAR ME?! BIG!!

YOU DON'T CALL A MIGHTY TREE **FAT!** IT'S **BIG!**

LOOK AT THAT MIGHTY TRUNK— JUST LOOK AT THOSE POWERFUL LIMBS — OPEN YOUR EYES!

JUST THINK OF ME AS A BIG, TOWERING, MAJESTIC NORTHERN PINE!

WELL, YOU GOT THE SAP, BABY.
4-20
DIK BROWNE
© King Features Syndicate, Inc., 1975. World rights reserved.

OUR LAND IS VERY BEAUTIFUL, ISN'T IT, DAD?
YES, MY SON. BUT IT IS MORE THAN THAT.

IT GIVES US EVERYTHING WE NEED FOR THE GOOD LIFE... TREES FOR BUILDING... BERRIES FOR EATING... ROCKS FOR THROWING...

LOOK, DAD! A STRANGER IS FISHING IN OUR POND!
NOW, NOW...

IT ISN'T **OUR** POND... THE GODS WHO MADE PONDS MADE THEM FOR ALL MEN TO SHARE.

THE SAME AS THE SUN, THE STARS AND THE MOON AND THE SOFT EVENING BREEZE ... DO YOU UNDERSTAND ?

AND BESIDES... THERE ARE NO FISH IN THAT POND...

LOOK!
I GOT ONE!

DIK BROWNE
11-23
STOP FISHING IN MY POND!!

IS THIS PUDDING GREAT?
YES, BUT IT COULD BE A BIT SWEETER
NOT FOR ME!

I ONLY WISH HAGAR WERE HALF THIS SWEET —
I'LL SAY!

HAGAR'S NOT SO BAD— HE'S GOT A HOT TEMPER — BUT HE DOESN'T HOLD A GRUDGE!

WHO ATE ALL THE WIFFENPOOF PUDDING?
WE DID. WHY?

THAT WAS MINE !!!
#!
BAM!
OW!
BOP!
SOCK!

BAM!
BOP!
SLAM!
OW!

SEE WHAT I MEAN?
LA-DE-DA
OH, WELL, FORGIVE AND FORGET...
5-2 DIK BROWNE

HI, THERE! I'M THE ENTERTAINMENT.
OH, GOOD. I'LL INTRODUCE YOU.

BUT FIRST LET ME GIVE YOU A TIP.
SWELL!

PEOPLE ARE TOUCHY THESE DAYS SO STAY AWAY FROM RELIGION OR POLITICS.

NOW WE'RE GOING TO HEAR A JOKE FROM KNUTE THE NUT.
GOOD EVENING, LADIES AND GERMS...

© King Features Syndicate, Inc., 1975. World rights reserved
THERE ONCE WAS A REAL STUPID VIKING. HE WAS SO DUMB THAT...

...ER...
DIK BROWNE

...ER... HE BECAME A TEACHER IN ENGLAND.
HEY... THAT'S GOOD.
REAL SATIRE!
CLEVER
YUK
YUK
YUK
6-15

BOY! THAT'S A BIGGIE!!

TELL THE MEN I'M READY TO ATTACK!

HAGAR! THE MEN ARE SKULKING WITH FEAR!
?

MEN! DO YOU NOT HAVE FIERCE VIKING BLOOD IN YOUR VEINS?!
I THINK SO
I DO
ME TOO
MAYBE

AND ARE YOU NOT PROTECTED BY THE SHIELDS OF THOR ?!
YEAH!
YEAH!

AND ARE YOU NOT ARMED WITH THE SINGING SWORDS OF STEEL?!
YOU BET!
RIGHT ON!
YEAH!

AND IS NOT HAGAR THE HORRIBLE YOUR LEADER?

5-25
SKULK!
SKULK!
SKULK!
SKULK!
DIK BROWNE

WHEN'S DINNER?

NOW

?

HELGA! COULD THIS BAKED PORCUPINE BE DONE A LITTLE BETTER?

WHY ARE THE DOGS ACTING SO FUNNY?
GEE, I DUNNO...

UNLESS HELGA IS SINGING AGAIN

LOVELY! LOVELY!

THANK YOU! WOULD YOU LIKE ANOTHER SONG?

LOVELY...
HEY! I ASKED WOULD YOU LIKE ANOTHER SONG?

EH? WHAT DID YOU SAY?
I SAID: WOULD YOU LIKE ANOTHER SONG?

I CERTAINLY WOULD
OH, VERY WELL...

LOVELY! LOVELY!

Just running down to the local store for some horribly good cartoon books, colour albums, calendars, diaries, reminder calendars, greeting cards and giftwrap and tags – all featuring me of course!

Why not join me before the barbarians get there!

Hagar Books to collect:

POCKET BOOKS
Hagar Tries Again
Hagar Has A Go
Hagar In A Fix
Hagar On The Rampage
Hagar Gets It All
Hagar In The Rough
Hagar Leads The Way
Hagar Takes A Break
Hagar All At Sea
Hagar On Holiday
Hagar Takes Aim
Hagar In A Stew

COLOUR ALBUMS
Hagar Lets Himself Go
Hagar The Hero

COLOUR CARTOON BOOKS
Hagar Tells It Like It Is
Hagar Never Say Die
Hagar Makes An Entrance
Hagar Welcome Home

BLACK + WHITE CARTOON BOOKS
Hagar Meets His Match
Hagar In A Hurry

Hagar The Horrible's Viking Handbook